Macmillan

English

Fluency Book

2

Mary Bowen
Printha Ellis
Louis Fidge
Liz Hocking
Wendy Wren

MACMILLAN

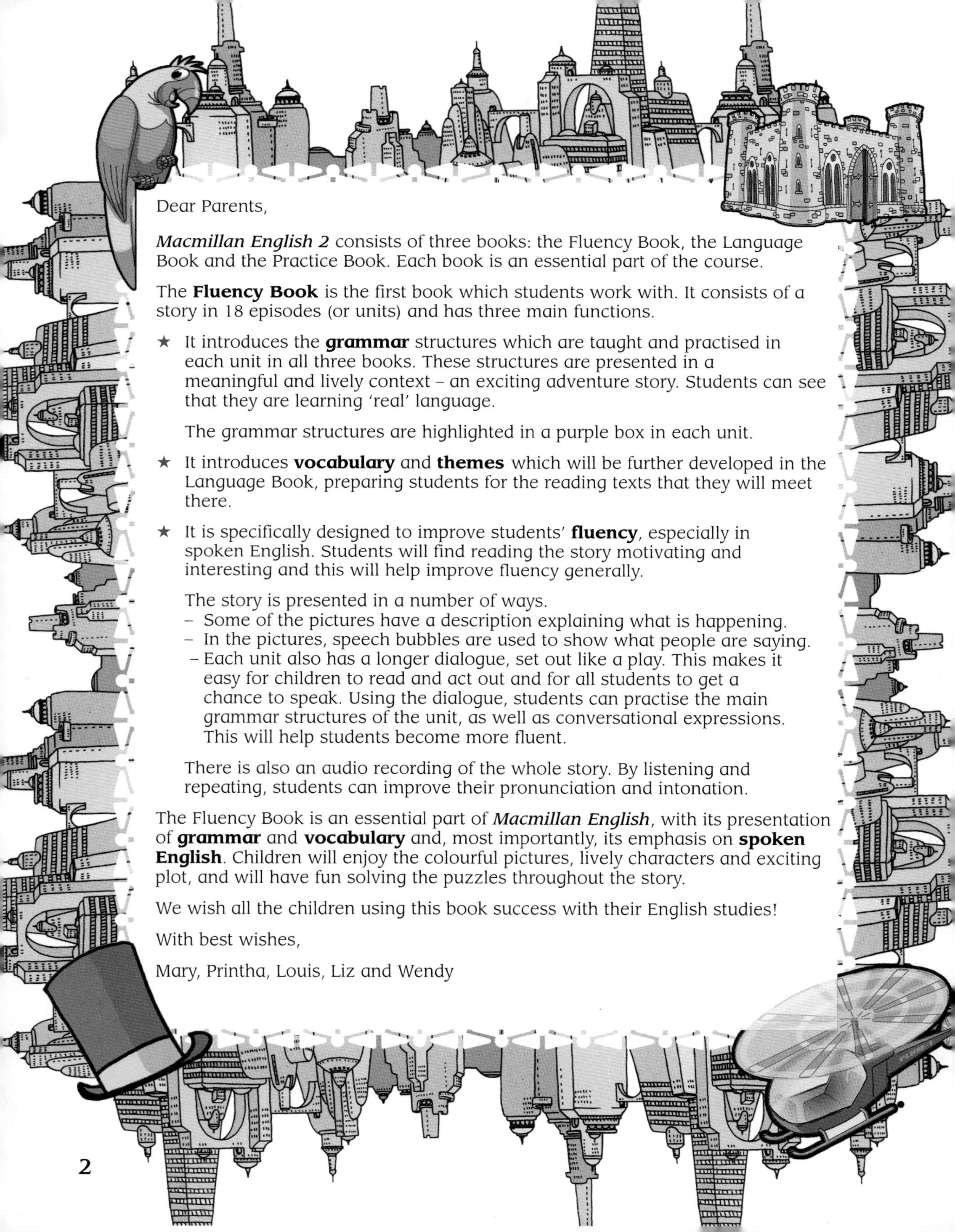

Dear Parents,

Macmillan English 2 consists of three books: the Fluency Book, the Language Book and the Practice Book. Each book is an essential part of the course.

The **Fluency Book** is the first book which students work with. It consists of a story in 18 episodes (or units) and has three main functions.

★ It introduces the **grammar** structures which are taught and practised in each unit in all three books. These structures are presented in a meaningful and lively context – an exciting adventure story. Students can see that they are learning 'real' language.

The grammar structures are highlighted in a purple box in each unit.

★ It introduces **vocabulary** and **themes** which will be further developed in the Language Book, preparing students for the reading texts that they will meet there.

★ It is specifically designed to improve students' **fluency**, especially in spoken English. Students will find reading the story motivating and interesting and this will help improve fluency generally.

The story is presented in a number of ways.

- Some of the pictures have a description explaining what is happening.
- In the pictures, speech bubbles are used to show what people are saying.
- Each unit also has a longer dialogue, set out like a play. This makes it easy for children to read and act out and for all students to get a chance to speak. Using the dialogue, students can practise the main grammar structures of the unit, as well as conversational expressions. This will help students become more fluent.

There is also an audio recording of the whole story. By listening and repeating, students can improve their pronunciation and intonation.

The Fluency Book is an essential part of *Macmillan English*, with its presentation of **grammar** and **vocabulary** and, most importantly, its emphasis on **spoken English**. Children will enjoy the colourful pictures, lively characters and exciting plot, and will have fun solving the puzzles throughout the story.

We wish all the children using this book success with their English studies!

With best wishes,

Mary, Printha, Louis, Liz and Wendy

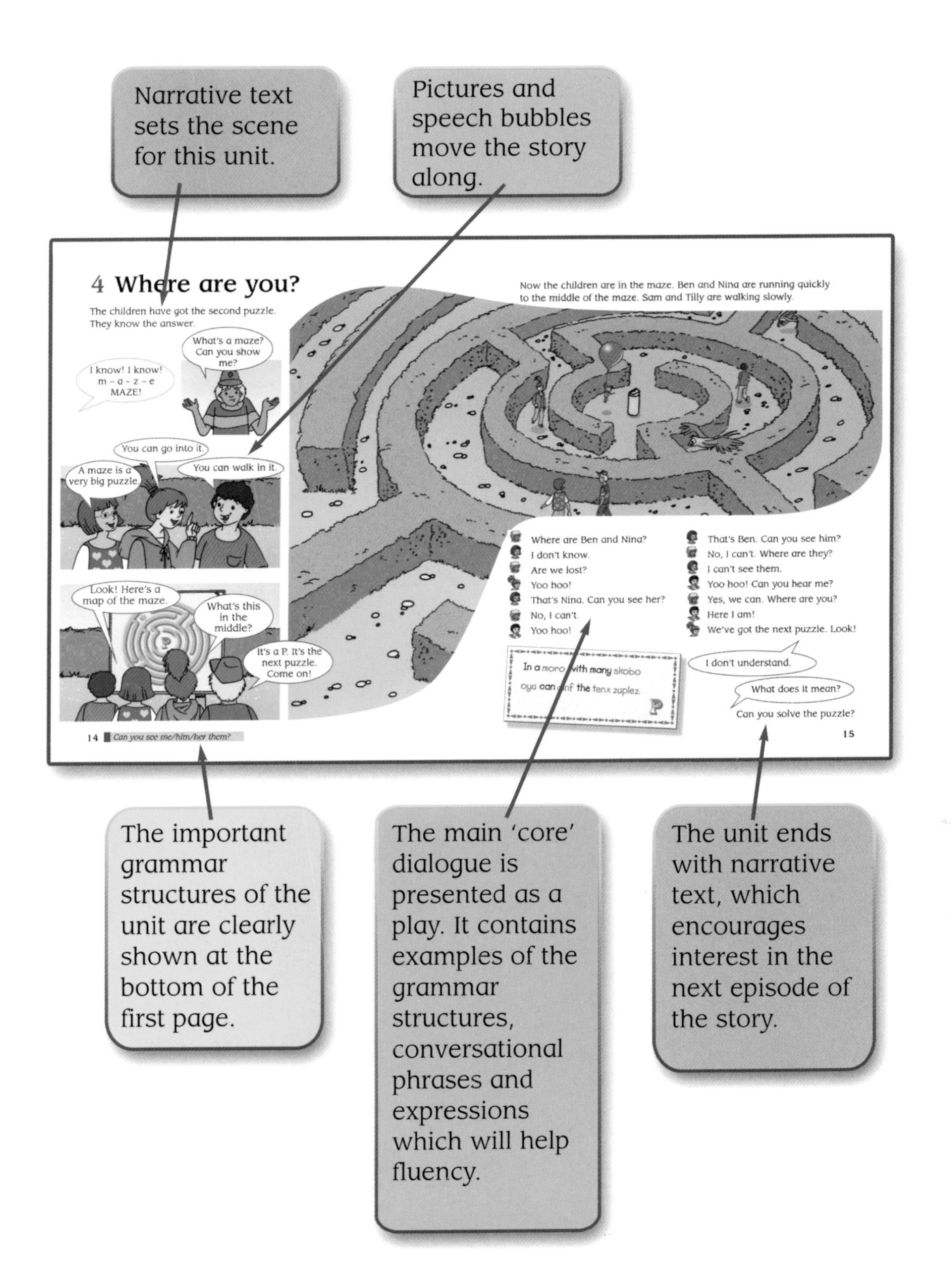
Narrative text sets the scene for this unit.
Pictures and speech bubbles move the story along.
4 Where are you?
The children have got the second puzzle. They know the answer.
What's a maze? Can you show me?
I know! I know! m – a – z – e MAZE!
You can go into it.
A maze is a very big puzzle.
You can walk in it.
Look! Here's a map of the maze.
What's this in the middle?
It's a P. It's the next puzzle. Come on!
14 Can you see me/him/her them?
Now the children are in the maze. Ben and Nina are running quickly to the middle of the maze. Sam and Tilly are walking slowly.
Where are Ben and Nina?
I don't know.
Are we lost?
Yoo hoo!
That's Nina. Can you see her?
No, I can't.
Yoo hoo!
That's Ben. Can you see him?
No, I can't. Where are they?
I can't see them.
Yoo hoo! Can you hear me?
Yes, we can. Where are you?
Here I am!
We've got the next puzzle. Look!
I don't understand.
What does it mean?
Can you solve the puzzle?
15
The important grammar structures of the unit are clearly shown at the bottom of the first page.
The main 'core' dialogue is presented as a play. It contains examples of the grammar structures, conversational phrases and expressions which will help fluency.
The unit ends with narrative text, which encourages interest in the next episode of the story.

Miss Plum
The Puzzler
Uncle Bob
Aunt Meg
Freddy
Polly
Ben
Mobi
Sam
Nina
Tilly

MUSEUM
HOSPITAL
SCHOOL
FUN HOUSE
THE GOLDEN LANTERN
THEATRE
BOATS
FOR
HIRE
SPORTS CLUB
PASCO'S
SUPERMARKET

Here is the city, the big noisy city.
Come with us! Come with us!
Here is the city, the big noisy city.
Come with us and play!

The vans and the cars and the buses on the street
And lots of funny people for you to meet.
Here is the city, the big noisy city.
Come with us and play!

The tower and the shops and the Fun House too,
The castle and the river are waiting for you!
Here is the city, the big noisy city.
Come with us and play!

Here is the city, the big noisy city.
Come with us! Come with us!
Here is the city, the big noisy city.
Come with us and play!

Welcome home!
Hello, Mum!
Hi!
Hi, Dad!
Hello!
PLUM-1
Mum, this is my friend, Sam.
You can come to our house, Sam.
Thanks!

1 An email from Dad

Nina is living with Aunt Meg and Uncle Bob. Her parents are in Canada. Her father is working there. Nina is looking out of the window. She can see the city below her. Uncle Bob is reading the newspaper. Aunt Meg is working on the computer. Her cousin Freddy is drawing a picture. Who is that at the door?

Sam, Ben and Tilly are standing outside the door. Polly the parrot is sitting on Sam's shoulder. Can you see Mobi? Where is he?

 He/She is reading. What are you doing?

 This is our new friend Sam.

 Hello, Sam.

 Hello.

 I'm Freddy. I'm four.

 He's my cousin.

 Hello, Freddy.

 Hello.

 What's that? Is it a TV?

 No, it isn't. It's a computer.

 Wow! And what's that?

 It's the mouse.

 What are you doing, Freddy?

 Hee hee hee!

 Oh, Freddy! You are naughty!

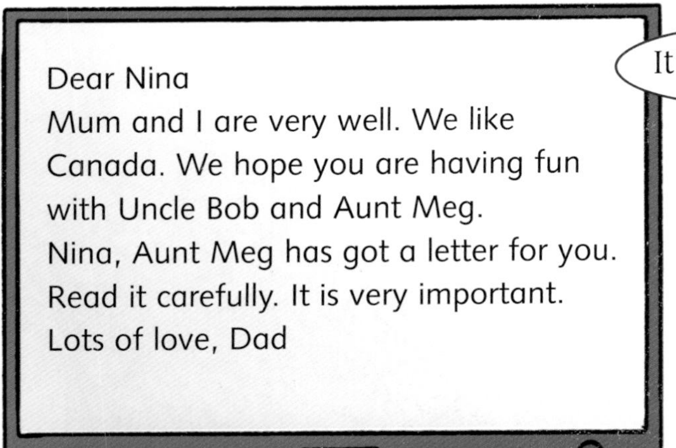
Dear Nina
Mum and I are very well. We like Canada. We hope you are having fun with Uncle Bob and Aunt Meg.
Nina, Aunt Meg has got a letter for you. Read it carefully. It is very important.
Lots of love, Dad

2 The first puzzle

Nina is reading the letter from her father.

Dear Nina,
A picture is missing from the City Museum. The thief is called The Puzzler.
He is a bad man but he is clever. He likes puzzles.
I think you and your friends can find the picture. You are clever too! Can you solve the puzzles? Can you find the missing picture?
Here is a picture of The Puzzler and here is his first puzzle. Good luck!

Lots of love,
Dad

picture? is Where the
to find you Do it? want
Sports Go the Club. to
can the You there.
next puzzle find

P

Can you solve the puzzle?

I like ... Do you like ... I don't like ...

Aunt Meg and the children are going to the Sports Club. The street is very busy. There are cars and buses and taxis. There are lorries and vans and bicycles. There are lots of people, too. It is very noisy. Nina, Tilly and Ben love the city. But what about Sam? Does he like it?

Barp! Barp!

Oh!

What's the matter, Sam?

It's very noisy.

Yes! It's great!

Do you like the city, Sam?

Well ... I don't like the noise and I don't like the crowds of people.

Beep! Beep!

And I don't like the cars.

Look! There's the Sports Club.

Come on! Let's find the next puzzle!

3 Welcome to our club

The children are at the Sports Club.

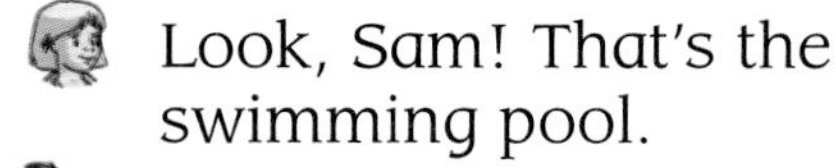
Look, Sam! That's the swimming pool.

Ben likes swimming.

You can play tennis here too.

Nina loves playing basketball.

I don't!

No, Tilly doesn't like it.

Look! That's the climbing wall.

What's that at the top?

It's a P! A big P!

P for The Puzzler!

It's the next puzzle!

I can get it!

Be careful, Ben!

Does Ben like climbing?

Yes, he does!

 He/She likes swimming. Does he/she like … ? He/She doesn't like …

Can you solve the puzzle?

4 Where are you?

The children have got the second puzzle.
They know the answer.

Now the children are in the maze. Ben and Nina are running quickly to the middle of the maze. Sam and Tilly are walking slowly.

Where are Ben and Nina?

I don't know.

Are we lost?

Yoo hoo!

That's Nina. Can you see her?

No, I can't.

Yoo hoo!

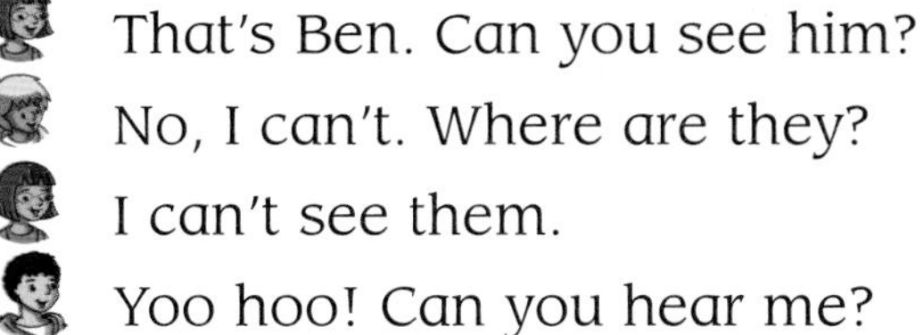

That's Ben. Can you see him?

No, I can't. Where are they?

I can't see them.

Yoo hoo! Can you hear me?

Yes, we can. Where are you?

Here I am!

We've got the next puzzle. Look!

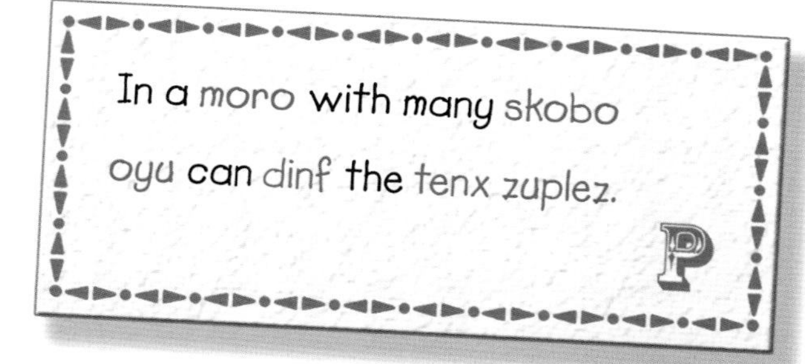

I don't understand.

What does it mean?

Can you solve the puzzle?

5 Time for school

The children have got the next puzzle.They can understand it now. Can you?

Nina, Tilly and Ben are going to school. Sam is going with them.

Do you go to school every day?

No, not every day.

We go five days a week.

What do you do at school?

We learn to write.

We learn to read too.

Are there lots of books in your school?

Oh, yes. Lots and lots.

We've got a big library.

Hey! That's it! Look at the puzzle!

'A room with many books.'

It's the library!

Is this your school?

Yes, it is.

Does the bus stop here?

Yes, it does.

It stops next to the gate.

Come on! Let's go to the library.

Does the bus stop here? Yes, it does./No, it doesn't.

Here is the next puzzle.
Can you understand it?

6 The city at night

The children are on the balcony of Aunt Meg's apartment. It is quarter past nine and it is dark.

I can see the river and the boats.
I can see the streets and the shops.
Is that our school?
Yes, I think so.
Is that the hospital?
Yes, it is. Uncle Bob works there.
What's his job?
He's a doctor.
What about Aunt Meg? What's her job?
She's a teacher.
Does she teach at your school?
No, she doesn't. She teaches little children.
I'm little. I'm four.
Hello, Freddy. What have you got?
A piece of paper. An aeroplane.
Oh no! It's the puzzle!
Don't throw it, Freddy!
Oh, Freddy! You are naughty!

 What's his/her job? He's/She's a ... He/She works ... He/She doesn't work ...

The plane is flying down to the ground.

Look at Polly the parrot!

Can Polly get the plane?
Can she get the puzzle?

7 The tower

Polly has got the paper plane.

I can solve the puzzle! Listen.

In the city there is a street.
In the street there is a tower.
At the top of the tower there is a big window.
From the window you can see a flag.
On the flag you can see a P.

The next day the children, Aunt Meg and Freddy go to the tower.

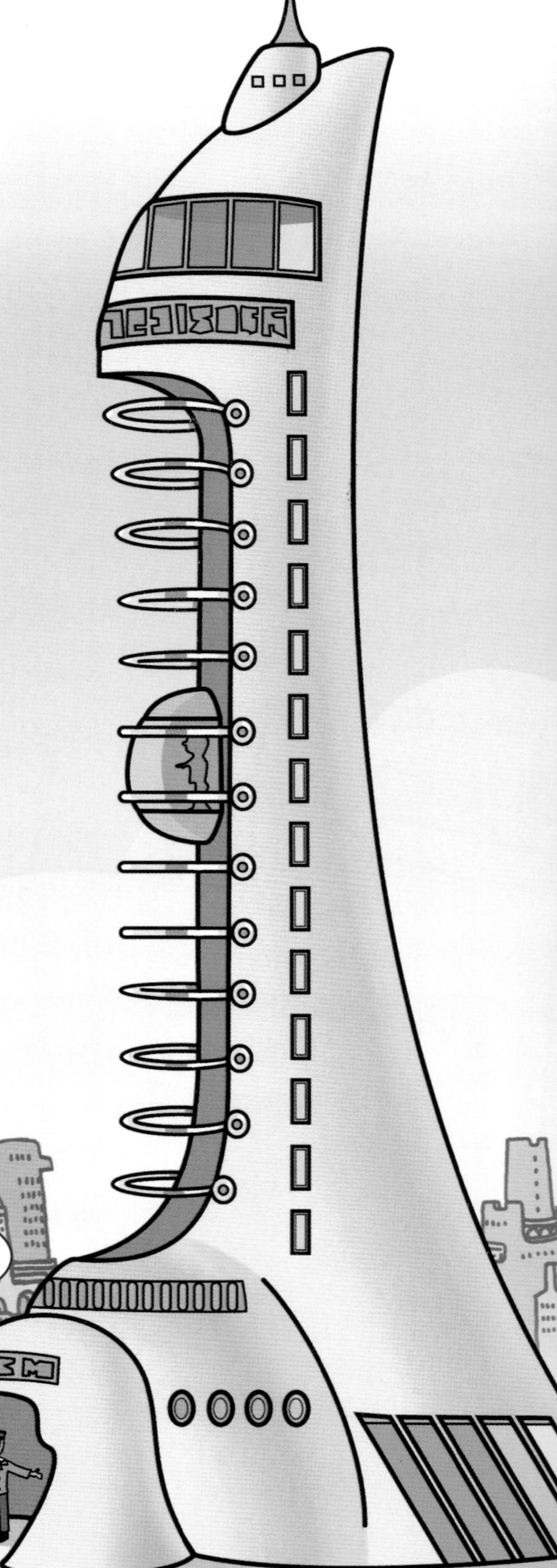

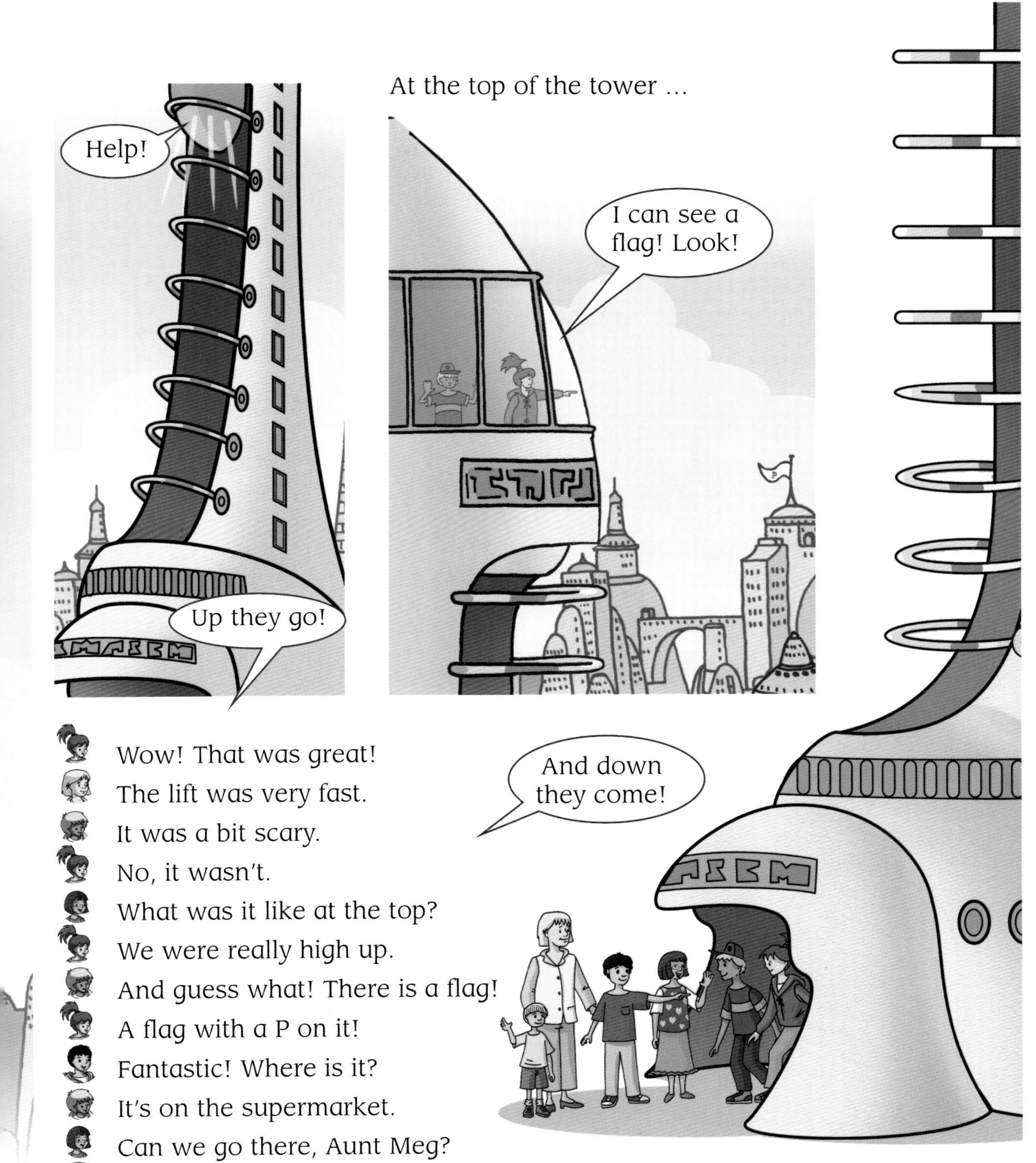

Wow! That was great!
The lift was very fast.
It was a bit scary.
No, it wasn't.
What was it like at the top?
We were really high up.
And guess what! There is a flag!
A flag with a P on it!
Fantastic! Where is it?
It's on the supermarket.
Can we go there, Aunt Meg?
Well ... all right. Come on.

Is the next puzzle at the supermarket?
Can the children find it?

8 At the supermarket

The children look at the fruit. But they can't find the puzzle. They look at the vegetables ...

We're looking for a p.

'p' for peach. 'p' for pear,

There's one 'p' in potato.

I've got it!

It was ... Was it ... ? It wasn't ... You/We were ... Were they ... ? We weren't ...

The children are very happy. They have got the next puzzle. Aunt Meg and Freddy are waiting for them.

There you are!

You were a long time.

No, we weren't. We were quick!

Look! We've got the next puzzle.

Was it in the peaches?

No, it wasn't!

Were the peaches very big and very nice?

Freddy likes peaches.

It wasn't in the peaches.

Was it in the peas?

Yes, it was. Well done, Freddy!

Let's look at it!

It's all numbers.

What a strange puzzle.

7.15 – 20.15 – 20.8.5 – 3.9.20.25 –
13.21.19.5.21.13

P

Can you solve the puzzle?

9 A phone call from Dad

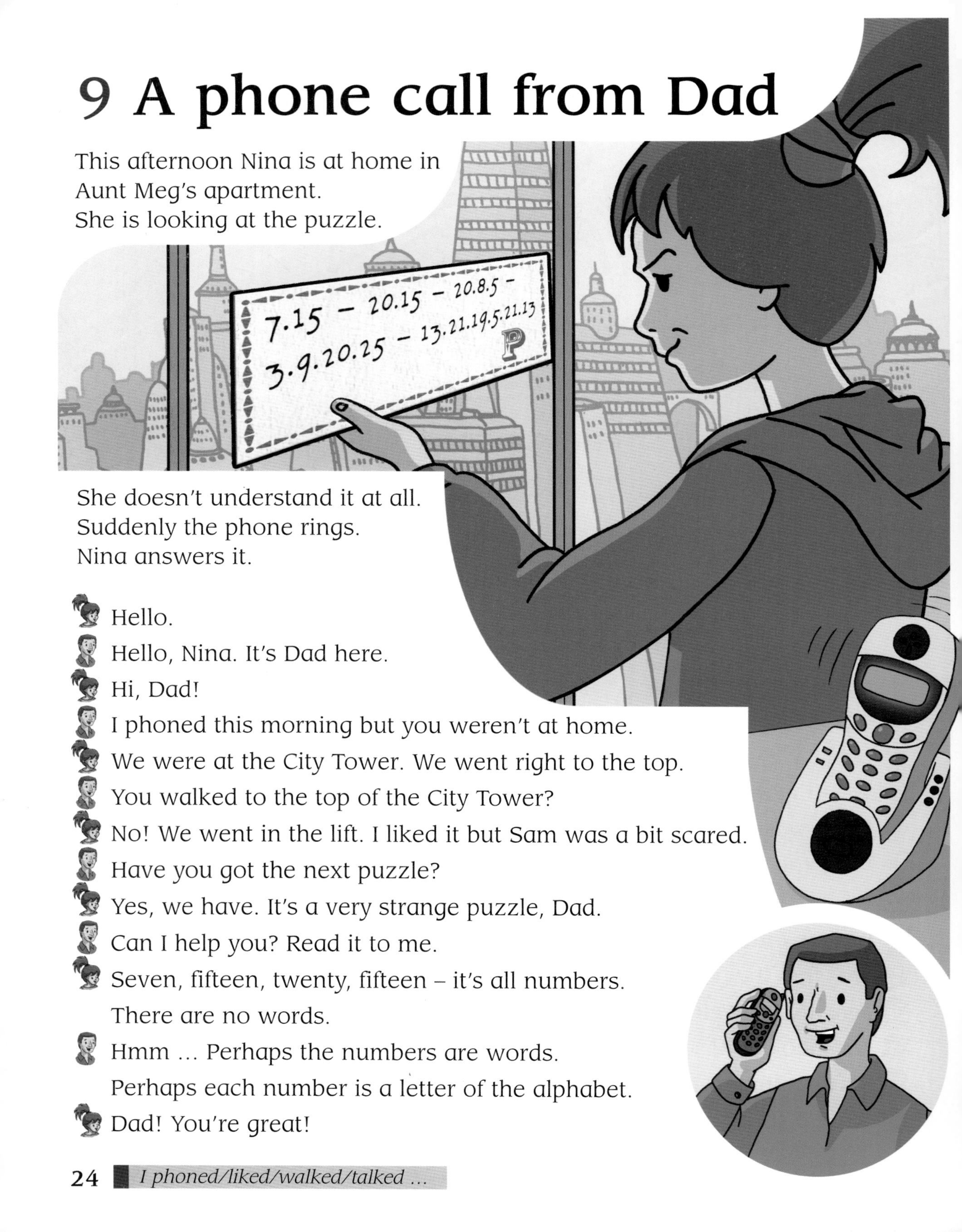

This afternoon Nina is at home in Aunt Meg's apartment.
She is looking at the puzzle.

She doesn't understand it at all.
Suddenly the phone rings.
Nina answers it.

Hello.

Hello, Nina. It's Dad here.

Hi, Dad!

I phoned this morning but you weren't at home.

We were at the City Tower. We went right to the top.

You walked to the top of the City Tower?

No! We went in the lift. I liked it but Sam was a bit scared.

Have you got the next puzzle?

Yes, we have. It's a very strange puzzle, Dad.

Can I help you? Read it to me.

Seven, fifteen, twenty, fifteen – it's all numbers.
There are no words.

Hmm ... Perhaps the numbers are words.
Perhaps each number is a letter of the alphabet.

Dad! You're great!

The children are very happy.
But the City Museum is a very big place.
How can they find the next puzzle there?

10 At the City Museum

This morning the children and Aunt Meg went to the City Museum.

The museum is huge.

How can we find the next puzzle here?

Let's go inside.

MUSEUM

 It is/It was ... They are/They were ... They lived ...

The children and Aunt Meg looked at 'People in the Past'. It was very interesting.

 Look! Here are the Incas.
They lived in Peru.

 Where's Peru?

 It's in South America.

 Look! Here are the Chinese!

 They were very clever.

 Here are the Egyptians.

 Wow! Look at the pyramids!
They're huge!

 What's this?

 It's old Egyptian writing.

 It's beautiful.

 There are lots of little pictures.

 People, animals, birds ...

 And the next puzzle! Look!

GO TO THE CAFE. SIT UNDER THE PALM TREE. P

Is it Egyptian writing?

The next puzzle was very, very strange. Can you understand it?

11 A quick snack

Nina looked at the puzzle and then she asked Aunt Meg a question.

The children and Aunt Meg went to the museum cafe. It was like a jungle. There were plants and flowers and trees. The cafe was crowded but one table was free. It was under a palm tree …

 Let's have a quick snack.

 Here's the menu.

 Let's see … What can we have?

 Burgers?

 Pizza?

 What about a nice sandwich?

 Did you like 'People in the Past', Sam?

 Yes, I did. It was very interesting.

 I liked the pyramids. They were huge!

Tilly! Look at the menu and choose your snack.

OK. Oh! This menu is very strange.

And that man was very strange!

Did you see him Nina?

No, I didn't.

I think he was The Puzzler!

Oh! The menu is a puzzle!

Can you solve the puzzle?

12 At the Fun House

That afternoon the children and Aunt Meg went to the Fun House. It was crowded and noisy. Aunt Meg did not like it. She went shopping.

I want to climb up the pyramid.
I want to swing across the river.
Mind the crocodiles!
Then I want to walk along that high rope.
Let's jump in the bouncy castle!
OK. Then we can go on the train!
But Tilly, where is the next puzzle?
Come on, you two!
We're in the Fun House. Let's have fun!

 He/She/They did not like/walk/find ...

Sam crossed the river on a swing. Tilly did not cross the river.

Ben climbed the pyramid. The next puzzle was not at the top.

Tilly and Nina jumped up and down in the bouncy castle.

Sam walked along the rope. Ben did not walk along it.

The girls liked the funny train. The boys did not like it.

13 Happy birthday!

The next day the children were at school. There was a chart on the board at the front of the classroom.

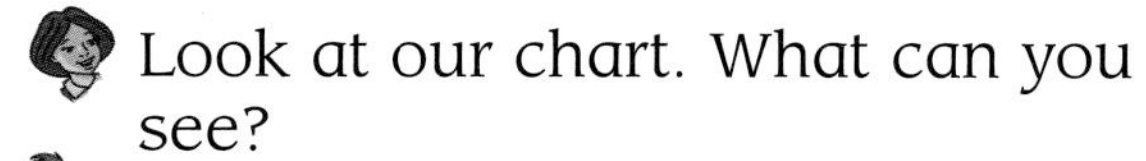

Look at our chart. What can you see?

The months of the year.

That's right. How many months are there?

There are twelve!

Very good! Ben, when's your birthday?

It's in July.

Go and write your name on the chart.

Next to July?

Yes, that's right. What about you, Tilly? When's your birthday?

It's today.

Close your eyes, Tilly. Now open them!

SURPRISE!
Oh, thank you!
There are cards.
And presents!
There's a big cake!
Happy birthday, Tilly!
HAPPY BIRTHDAY, TILLY!
Let's play the birthday game!
When it's your birthday, please stand up!
January February March …
When it's your birthday, please sit down!
January February March …
HAPPY BIRTHDAY!
Ta keaw alk byt
heri vera ndlo ok
att hebo ats
P
Tilly! Here's another card. Open it!
Oh! Here's the next puzzle!
Can you solve the puzzle?

14 A walk by the river

The message was 'Take a walk by the river and look at the boats.'
After school the children went to the river with Aunt Meg and Freddy. It was a sunny afternoon. There were lots of people by the river. Women walked along with their babies. Children played under the trees.

'Look at the boats.' That was the message.

Are there any boats?

Yes, Freddy. Over there.

I can't see any boats!

Look, Freddy! On the other side of the river.

There are some flags on the boats.

What's on the flags?

I can't see. Give me your telescope, Freddy!

What can you see?

Guess what? There's a 'P' on one of the flags.

But how can we cross the river?

I can row across the river!

 Are/Were there any … ? There are/There were some … I haven't got/I can't see any …

There were two men on the steps by the river.

The next puzzle was on the flag.

Here is the puzzle. Can you understand it?

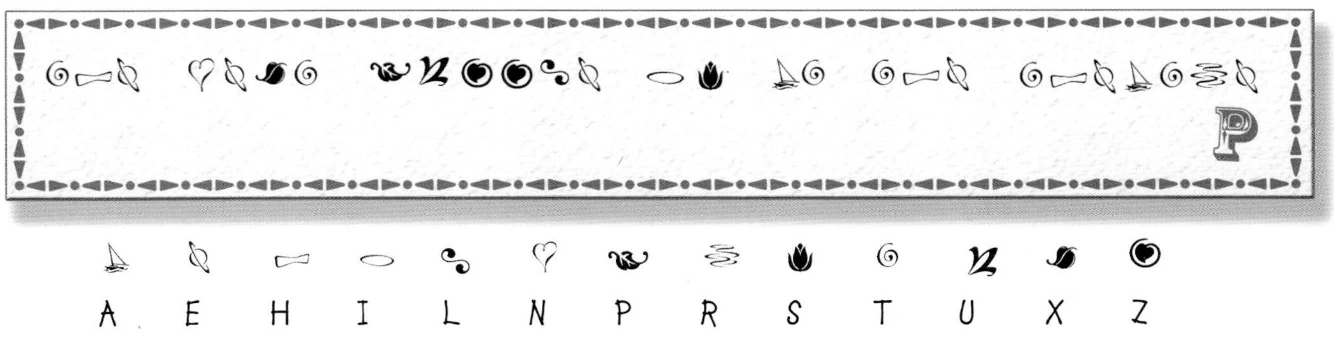

15 At the theatre

The message was 'The next puzzle is at the theatre.' That evening the children went to the City Theatre. Uncle Bob went with them. The show was called 'Children of the World!'

This is a great show, Sam.
Yes, it's good fun.
There are lots of children in the show.
Some of them sing.
Some of them dance.
Some of them play the piano.
Don't forget Mr Amazing!
Who is Mr Amazing?
He's very clever.
What does he do?
Wait and see!

The show was great! There was singing. There was dancing. Some children played the piano ...

 Whose ... is this? It is mine/yours/his/hers.

and then there was Mr Amazing.

Was it Tilly's bag? Yes, it was hers.

Was it Ben's watch? Yes, it was his.

Here is the puzzle. Can the children solve it? Can you solve it?

16 At the castle

The message from The Puzzler was: 'Go to the castle. The picture is in the Red Tower.' The next day the children went to the castle with Aunt Meg. The castle had four towers. Where was the Red Tower?

Look! Here's a map.
Where's the Red Tower?
I can see the Blue Tower.
Here's the Black Tower.
And here's the White Tower ...
Look! The Red Tower! Here it is!
How do we get to it?
We're here, in front of the big door.
Go through the big door and turn right.
Go through the little door and turn left.
Go straight on ...
And then we come to the Red Tower!
Come on! Let's go!

The children went into the tower. They saw some stone steps. The steps went up and up.

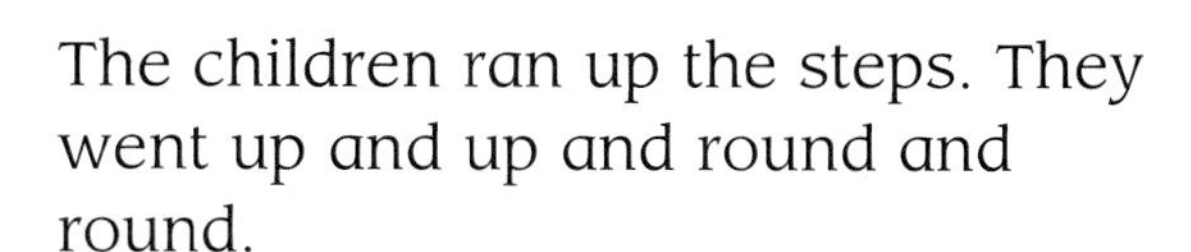
The children ran up the steps. They went up and up and round and round.

At the top of the steps there was a small red door.

They opened the door and went into a small room.

The missing picture was not there. The room was empty but there were strange letters on the wall. What did they mean? Do you know? What can the children do now?

17 Well done, Ben!

The children looked at the letters. They did not understand.
Then Tilly had an idea. She touched the letters one by one.

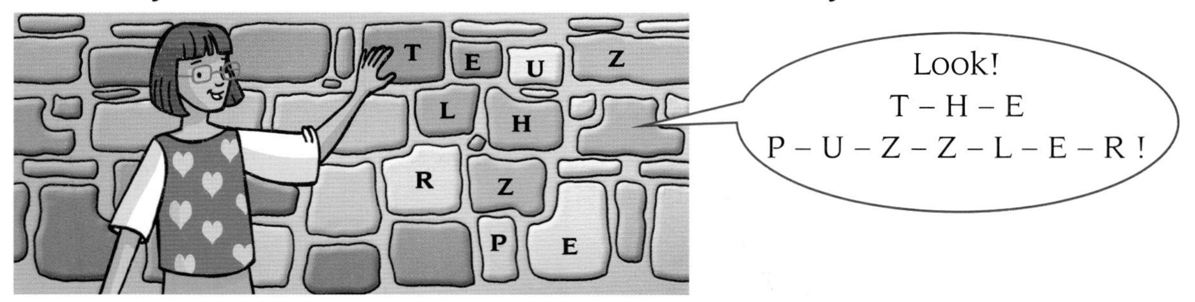

Tilly put her hand on the last letter – the letter R. The big stones moved.
Ben went into the hole.

Ben came out of the hole. What did he have? He had the missing picture!

Where did you find it? I found it. They did not understand.

The children were very happy. They ran quickly down the steps of the Red Tower.

Aunt Meg! Aunt Meg! We've got the picture!

Oh! That's wonderful! Where did you find it?

There was a little room at the top of the tower.

There were letters on the wall.

The letters spelled 'The Puzzler'.

Tilly touched the letters.

And the stones moved!

The picture was behind the wall.

I found it!

Well done, Ben! Now, let's look at this picture.

I like it.

What is the Golden Lantern? What is the surprise? Can you guess?

18 A big surprise

The Golden Lantern was a Chinese restaurant. It was Nina's favourite restaurant.

They went inside. A waiter greeted them.

The waiter took them to a long table next to the window. There were some people at the table. Who were they?

It was Nina's mum and dad.

Nina gave them a big hug.

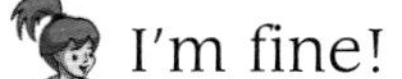

Hello, Nina!

How are you?

I'm fine!

Tell me about the picture.

Where did you find it?

We found it in the Black Tower.

No, we didn't.

We found it in the Red Tower.

Well, you are very clever children.

Now let's have a lovely dinner.

What about The Puzzler, Dad?

Who is he?

Where is he?

Oh! Look at the window!

It's The Puzzler!

It's time to say goodbye, goodbye from the city.
Say goodbye! Wave goodbye!
It's time to say goodbye, goodbye from the city.
Goodbye! See you soon!
Run!
We went to the museum and the maze in the park,
The theatre and the castle with its tower so dark.
It's time to say goodbye, goodbye from the city.
Goodbye! See you soon!
Wait for me!

We found all the puzzles and we solved them too.
We found the missing picture and so did you.
It's time to say goodbye, goodbye from the city.
Goodbye! See you soon!

It's time to say goodbye, goodbye from the city.
Say goodbye! Wave goodbye!
It's time to say goodbye, goodbye from the city.
Goodbye! See you soon!

The missing picture

Make the missing picture! Stick your stickers here!

Can you name all the missing things in the picture?
They all begin with 'P'. Write the words here.

P

Wordlist

Unit 1: aunt, city, computer, cousin, door, email, letter, mouse, newspaper, parents, picture, uncle, window; important, naughty; carefully; draw, live, stand, work

Come in! Come here!

Unit 2: bicycle, bus, car, city, crowd, lorry, love, museum, noise, people, puzzle, Sports Club, street, taxi, thief, van;; bad, busy, clever, easy, first, next, noisy; solve, stay

Good luck! I don't understand. What about ... ? What's the matter?

Unit 3: basketball, climbing, climbing wall, swimming, swimming pool, tennis

Welcome! What does it mean?

Unit 4: answer, maze, middle, park, path; second, lost; quickly, slowly; know, show

Don't get lost! Here I am!

Unit 5: gate, library, school; every; learn, look for, read, write

Unit 6: aeroplane, apartment, balcony, building, doctor, hospital, job, paper, piece

I think so.

Unit 7: flag, lift, supermarket, tower; fast, high, scary

Guess what! Well ... all right

Unit 8: bread, fruit, pea, peach, pear, pineapple, plum, vegetables; long, nice; over there

There you are!

Unit 9: afternoon, alphabet, letter, museum, number, phone call, place, word; fantastic, strange; at home; answer, phone, ring, talk, walk

Unit 10: dinosaur, monster, past, pyramid, writing; beautiful, Egyptian, huge, interesting

Wait for me!

Unit 11: burger, cheese, chicken, chips, cola, menu, mirror, orange juice, palm tree, pizza, plant, question, snack, chocolate; crowded, delicious, free, strawberry, super, tasty, yummy; ask, choose

Here it is. Stop talking!

Unit 12: message, rope, swing, train; silly; cross, make, go shopping, meet

Unit 13: birthday, board, card, chart, classroom, game, month, present, year; January, February, March, April, May, June, July, August, September, October, November, December; close, open

Happy birthday! Surprise!

Unit 14:
babies, men, money, side, telescope, women; row; after

Don't worry!

Unit 15: evening, piano, show, theatre, world; watch

Wait and see!

Unit 16: map; empty; in front of, behind, through

Turn right/left. Go straight on.

Unit 17: idea, pocket, stone; wonderful, golden; move, touch

Unit 18: dinner, restaurant, hug; favourite, hungry; follow, give, take, tell